D0854121

This Hannah Montana Annual belongs to:

....

My top three Hannah Montana songs are:

1 ....
2 ....
3 ....

Disney

HANNAH MONTANA

ANNUAL 2010

EGMONT

We bring stories to life

First published in Great Britain 2009
by Egmont UK Limited,
239 Kensington High Street, London W8 6SA
© Disney Enterprises, Inc.
Based on the series created by Michael Poryes and
Rich Correll & Barry O'Brien

Based on the episode, "That's What Friends Are For," Written by Douglas Lieblein
Based on the episode, "Me and Mr Jonas and Mr Jonas and Mr Jonas,"
Written By Douglas Lieblein
Based on the episode, "Achy Jakey Heart, Part Two," Written by Andrew Green

Editor: Nina Filipek
Designer: Dan Green

ISBN 978 1 4052 4651 4

1 3 5 7 9 10 8 6 4 2

Printed in Italy

All rights reserved. No part of this publication may be reproduced, stored in a
retrieval system, or transmitted, in any form or by any means, electronic, mechanical,
photocopying, recording or otherwise, without the prior permission of the publisher
and copyright owner.

Note to parents: adult supervision is recommended when
sharp-pointed items such as scissors are in use.

WHAT'S

INSIDE

Who's Who

Miley Stewart
AKA: Hannah Montana

Miley is an ordinary teen most of the time, but by night she's the one and only Hannah Montana, pop princess. With a string of successful hit songs and adoring fans everywhere, she's a one-in-a-million pop sensation.

But Hannah has a big secret: her fans don't know that she's also Miley Stewart and Miley's school mates (except a few of her closest friends) don't know she's also Hannah! And that's why her life gets sooo complicated. Though she wouldn't want it any other way!

Write three things you like best about Miley.

1
....
....
....
....
....

2
....
....
....
....
....

3
....
....
....
....
....

Draw a new stage outfit for Hannah.

Who's Who

Lilly Truscott
AKA: Lola Luftnagle

Lilly is Miley's best friend. She was a big Hannah Montana fan before she knew about Miley's secret. It was when she bluffed her way into Hannah's dressing room after a concert one night that Hannah decided to tell Lilly the truth.

Now Lilly enjoys going to Hannah's concerts as Lola Luftnagle. This skater-girl sure is one crazy friend!

Write three things you like best about Lilly.

1 ....
....
....
....
....

2 ....
....
....
....
....

3 ....
....
....
....
....

Draw a new stage outfit for Lola Luftnagle.

11

Who's Who

Oliver Oken

Once upon a time Oliver had a massive crush on Hannah Montana. He didn't realise she was his friend Miley and when he found out the truth he didn't take it too well. In fact, he fainted! Not a cool look for Oliver!

Now he's just about over it and he, Lilly and Miley are the best of friends.

Write three things you like best about Oliver.

1 ....
....
....

2 ....
....
....

3 ....
....
....

Rico

Rico goes to the same school as Miley, Lilly and Oliver. In fact, he's now in the same class because he skipped a few grades. Rico's a smart kid but he drives the others mad with his wild ideas and wacky sense of humour. He runs the Surf Shop where Miley's brother Jackson works after school.

Write three things you like best about Rico.

1 ....
....

2 ....
....

3 ....
....

Who's Who

Jackson Rod Stewart

Jackson is Miley's big brother. He's proud of his famous little sister but this doesn't stop him from teasing her 24/7. Jackson's a number-one prankster and he and his dad are constantly trying to get the better of each other. But more often than not, Jackson comes out the loser!

Write three things you like best about Jackson.

1 ....
....
....

2 ....
....
....

3 ....
....
....

Robby Ray Stewart

Robby is Jackson and Miley's dad. He's also a talented musician and songwriter. In fact, he writes Hannah's songs and manages her glittering career. Robby is proud of the Stewart family's southern roots and loves to reminisce about Uncle Earl and Aunt Pearl back home in Tennessee – much to Miley's embarrassment!

Write three things you like best about Robby.

1 ....

....

....

2 ....

....

....

3 ....

....

....

Hannah's World

Find these words hidden in this Hannah wordsearch.

CONCERT	DISCUISE	FASHION
SECRET	GLITTER	FRIENDS
FANS	WARDROBE	DANCE
STAGE	GUITAR	SUPERSTAR

```
S E C R E T V G B T P T
D W S G R V Y P M N L S
T Z A U E S I U G S I D
G L F R P F M Q H S Y N
F L Q L D E Q D A N C E
G U I T A R R P L P G I
J T S T W Q O S N M M R
K S V M T W S B T C K F
M S T A G E Q K E A K K
P W V S G X R Y L I R C
T R E C N O C Q F A N S
F A S H I O N T R R L E
```

Now check out the answers on page 67.

Guitar Girl

Miley loves her guitars. How many guitars can you find hidden in the picture?

Answer

Answers on page 67.

Superstar

So, you think you're pretty sharp ... well, here's a test! See how quickly you can find 10 differences in the second picture.

1

Doubles

2

Answers on page 67.

THAT'S WHAT FRIENDS ARE FOR

Read this scene taken from a favourite Hannah Montana show. Write the missing names in the gaps by choosing from the list. Check out your answers on page 67.

The Cast:

Miley   **Lilly**   **Jake**   **Mikayla**

Jake surprised [1]_____ by turning up on her doorstep one day.

Miley thought he wanted to get back with her but [2]_____ said,

"I just want to be friends." [3]_____ pretended she was cool with

it. "This is great! I would love to be friends!" she replied.

"There's no way you and

Heartbreak [4]_____ can

be friends," said [5]_____.

Then Miley found out that

Jake's co-star in his next

movie was her rival,

[6]_____. When Jake

told her that every scene was, "... kiss, kiss, kiss, kiss ..." [7]_____

plotted to get Mikayla fired. First, she managed to lock Mikayla off

the set by saying that someone was waiting for her outside. Then

she disguised herself in an identical alien costume and make-up so

that everyone thought she was [8]_____.

Second, she insulted [9]_____ and messed up their lines,

until Jake couldn't take any more. "I want her fired!" he yelled.

When the real [10]_____ finally returned to the set, she had

trouble convincing everyone who she was. Then Mikayla and Miley

met face to face and [11]_____ was busted. Back home, later

that day, she had to face her dad, then Jake. He stormed in.

"I cannot believe what you did!" said [12]_____.

"Last time you were the one with some growing up to do, and now

it's my turn. But if I promise not to wreck another movie, can

we try to be friends again?" asked [13]_____. "I'd like that,"

said Jake. Miley and Lilly apologised to [14]_____. She said she

understood and wanted to be friends with [15]_____! "We can

do all of my fave things: shop, get our nails done, and talk about

how much I hate Hannah Montana!" [16]_____ said.

Would You Rather...?

Have you ever found yourself stuck with two crummy choices? It's so not fair! But if you had to decide one way or the other, would you rather ...

Circle your answers!

1.	Eat cold sprouts?	OR	Bathe in cold water?
2.	Have toothache?	OR	Have the flu?
3.	Face detention for a week?	OR	Go out with a geek?
4.	Look seriously uncool?	OR	Do extra homework?
5.	Miss a great party?	OR	Miss the school bus?
6.	Smell of garlic?	OR	Smell of disinfectant?
7.	Wear a little kid's rain hat?	OR	Wear a clown's outfit?
8.	Admit you're wrong?	OR	Pay a fine?

Would Miley Rather...?

Sometimes in life, we have to make difficult choices and no one knows that better than Miley! What would she rather do in these seriously gross situations? You can decide for her!

1.	**Kiss a chimp?**	**OR**	**Kiss Rico?**
2.	**Miss a big concert?**	**OR**	**Miss her bro's birthday?**
3.	**Tell her secret?**	**OR**	**Swim with crocodiles?**
4.	**Ride a Bucking Bronco?**	**OR**	**Ride a bike with stabilisers?**
5.	**Go on a date with Rico?**	**OR**	**Cover her face in cream pie?**
6.	**Be best mates with Ashley?**	**OR**	**Wear a fake moustache?**
7.	**Hug Amber?**	**OR**	**Hug an octopus?**
8.	**Say nothing for a day?**	**OR**	**Use Jackson's towel?**

Trivia Tick Test

Take this tick test to find out how much you know about the show 'Achy Jakey Heart, Part 1'.

1. What gossip are the tabloid magazines spreading about Hannah?

☐ **a)** That Hannah's dating Oliver

☐ **b)** That Hannah is a guy

☐ **c)** That Hannah is Miley

2. How does Jake ask Miley to take him back?

☐ **a)** He parachutes out of the sky and presents Miley with a rose and chocolates

☐ **b)** He leaps out of a limo and presents Miley with tickets to his premiere

☐ **c)** He rides up on a horse and presents Miley with a teddy bear

3. Jake sends Miley a life-size cut-out of himself. What's written on the front?

☐ **a)** I ♥ Me

☐ **b)** I ♥ Hannah Montana

☐ **c)** I ♥ Miley

4. Why can't Jake take Miley to the premiere of his movie?

☐ **a)** He has to take his co-star

☐ **b)** He's taking Mikayla

☐ **c)** He's taking Hannah

5. Who interviews Jake at the premiere?

- ☐ **a)** Oliver Oken
- ☐ **b)** Brian Winters
- ☐ **c)** Robby Stewart

6. Miley becomes famous for being Jake's girlfriend. Which two people are the first to want to be her new friends?

- ☐ **a)** Amber and Ashley
- ☐ **b)** Rico and Oliver
- ☐ **c)** Cooper and Roxy

7. When Jackson and Oliver start their own snack shack, what do they sell?

- ☐ **a)** Hot dogs
- ☐ **b)** Cheese jerky
- ☐ **c)** Cheesecake

8. Jake tells Miley a secret. What is it?

- ☐ **a)** His real name is Presley
- ☐ **b)** His real name is Wesley
- ☐ **c)** His real name is Leslie

9. Why can't Miley go on a date with Jake the following day?

- ☐ **a)** She's reading to second graders
- ☐ **b)** She's recording a song
- ☐ **c)** She's got a concert in Florida

10. When Miley told Jake she had a secret too, what did Jake reply?

- ☐ **a)** "Your middle name is Leslie?"
- ☐ **b)** "You're moving to Peru?"
- ☐ **c)** "You're not married, are you?"

Answers on page 67.

Are You a Best

Take the test to find out if your friendship will last. Tick the statements below that best describe your friendship.

We'd hate to turn up at a party in the same dress.

We love going shopping together.

We don't do our homework together.

We love doing each other's hair.

We are sometimes jealous of each other.

We've been on holiday together.

We both have lots of other friends.

We borrow each other's clothes.

We are opposites really.

Count up the stars: ☐ stars **Count up the butterflies:** ☐ butterflies

28

Friend Forever?

We don't see each other at the weekend.

We're always having sleepovers.

We dream of sharing a house one day.

We look out for each other.

We share our secrets.

We sometimes get on each other's nerves.

We don't like the same music.

We're always fighting over something.

We laugh at each other's jokes.

Mostly Stars:

You both have strong personalities and often disagree about stuff. But, hey, Lilly and Miley are different and they get along like a house on fire! Sometimes you'll have to respect each other's views and give a bit more of your time to keep this friendship on track.

Mostly Butterflies:

You're like two peas in a pod: your friendship runs deep and true. But often when you're so close you shut others out and that can become stifling. If you can give each other a bit more space, it's likely that you'll still be friends when you're much, much older.

29

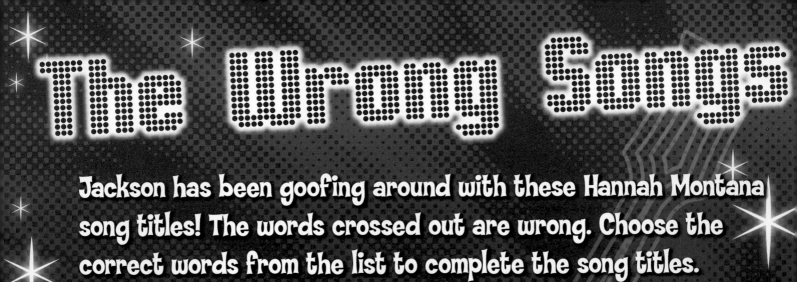

The Wrong Songs

Jackson has been goofing around with these Hannah Montana song titles! The words crossed out are wrong. Choose the correct words from the list to complete the song titles.

Choose from:

Friend	One
Party	Old
Star	Perfect
You	Noise

1. Make Some ~~Cakes~~

Make Some ⬜

2. We Got The ~~Money~~

We Got The ⬜

3. Nobody's ~~Fool~~

Nobody's [_____]

4. Rock ~~Chick~~

Rock [_____]

5. ~~New~~ Blue Jeans

[_____] Blue Jeans

6. ~~Tu~~ And Me Together

[_____] And Me Together

7. ~~Two~~ In A Million

[_____] In A Million

8. True ~~Jackson~~

True [_____]

Answers on page 68.

Hannah Styling

Check out Hannah's new look. It's seriously pop, rock and glam!

We love the pink signature fingerless glove!

Bright colours on a black background give this dress a modern touch of glamour.

Statement ring-bling!

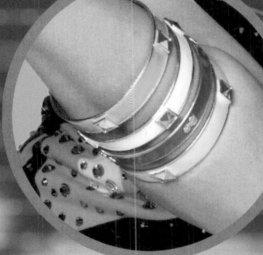

Bangles in coordinating colours look cool.

An essential extra — glossy turquoise footless tights!

These metallic silver shoe boots with a sculpted wedge are sensational!

Step Up to the

Follow the stars to get from Miley to Hannah before the concert begins. Play with a friend to find out who will be first in the spotlight at the end of the game!

Rules:

Play with one or two friends.

Take turns to roll the dice.

Don't cheat on the forfeits!

Throw an exact number to finish!

8
Quote from one of your fave Hannah Montana shows. Move on 3.

7

6
Jackson hogs the bathroom. Move back 1.

1
START

2
Miley gets an A for her English essay! Roll the dice again!

3

4
Miley and Lilly fall out big time! Go back to the start!

5

Spotlight

9

10 Hannah's new dress doesn't fit. Miss a turn!

11

12 Make up a new dance routine for Hannah. Move on 3!

13

14 Hannah loses an earring. Move back 1.

15

16 The limo's early. Move on 1.

17

18 Name five Hannah Montana songs. Roll the dice again!

19

20 FINISH

Dream On!

Miley's had some pretty strange dreams. Remember when she dreamt that Jackson was a famous rock star called Bucky Kentucky and she was just a piece of furniture? Luckily, her mum was in her dream, too, and she explained to Miley what her dream meant ...

Miley's dream

Miley was scared that if she lost her voice, she might lose her friends, too. Her mum reminded her that no matter what happened to her voice she had the most important thing a person can have – people who cared about her.

Discover what your dreams mean!

Being chased

Have you ever had a scary chase dream where you're running away from someone? This dream means you're feeling stressed about stuff. You might be stressing about school or quarrelling with a best friend. Try to sort out what's bugging you and chase this dream away.

Falling

You might have falling dreams at times when you're feeling insecure and unloved. Maybe you've flunked a grade at school or you've been made to look a fool in front of your mates. Arrange to go out with your friends and have some fun, and you'll soon be feeling good about yourself again!

Flying

Flying dreams are when you dream that you're flying and soaring like a bird, above trees, houses, clouds and everything else. They are awesome dreams to have because they make you feel powerful. You've got to be feeling really successful and on top of things to have flying dreams.

Failing an exam

This is when you dream you're failing an exam because you haven't revised or you've run out of time. It's a sign that you're lacking in confidence, you're worried that you're not good enough or that you're going to let others down. This doesn't mean you are going to fail! Usually, it's just the opposite!

Some people think that dreaming about animals can predict the future!

Horse
Sign of happiness!

Cat
Watch your enemies!

Barking dog
Brings bad news.

Happy dog
Brings many friends!

Eagle
Fame and wealth!

Flies
Annoying friends!

Rat
Trouble to come!

Whale
Good times!

Sweet Dreams

Capture your bad dreams in this cool dream catcher to ensure all your dreams are sweet!

What you do:

Top tip: Space out the loops and leave them fairly loose.

You will need:

- old embroidery ring
- embroidery thread or wool
- embroidery needle
- beads, cloth, fake fur and feathers

1.

Join the end of the thread to the embroidery ring with a knotted loop. To make the web, wind the thread around the ring, looping over and under all the way round. Make about 12 loops.

3.

Keep looping the thread through to make further rows. Continue until you have a small circular space in the middle of the web.

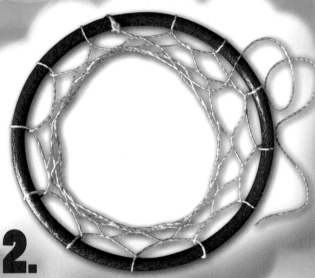

2.

Make another row of loops, going over and under the first row. Continue with a third row.

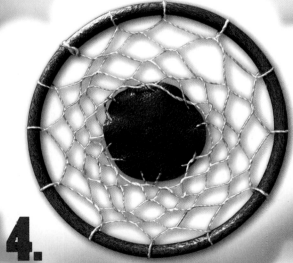

4.

Sew a piece of cloth and fake fur into the space at the centre. String together some beads and feathers on to separate lengths of thread and tie them to the bottom of the ring.

5.

Tie a loop of thread to the top of the finished dream catcher and hang above your bed for sweet dreams!

ACT IT OUT

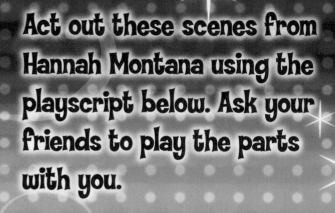

Act out these scenes from Hannah Montana using the playscript below. Ask your friends to play the parts with you.

Me and Mr Jonas and Mr Jonas and Mr Jonas

Hannah Montana and Robby are waiting outside the recording studio. Someone's in there and they're running late. Hannah is worried that if she doesn't start her recording session soon she'll miss the Shoe Sale later that day. She marches into the studio to find out who's keeping her waiting ...

HANNAH: Sweet mamma! It's the Jonas Brothers! Daddy! I told you somebody was in here. I'm so sorry, guys. He gets so impatient.

ROBBY: Sorry, fellas. I've got a big Shoe Sale I need to get to.

NICK: Dudes, it's Hannah Montana!

KEVIN: We're such big fans.

JOE: We love your music.

NICK: You're pretty ... Pretty good with the singing and the dancing that you do.

KEVIN: Nice save. (turns to Hannah) I'm Kevin.

HANNAH: The cute, romantic one. And you're Joe, the cute, funny one. You're Nick, the cute, sensitive one. (says to each brother in turn)

ROBBY: And I'm her daddy, the cute, protective one.

JOE: You're Robby Ray! He writes all the songs!

KEVIN: I know! 'Nobody's Perfect' is genius.

ROBBY: (jokes to Hannah) I like the cute, romantic one!

JOE: I love how it starts all soft, then BAM!

They burst into song.

ROBBY: (to Hannah) I was wrong. I like them all!

The Jonas Brothers ask Robby if he would write a song for them. Miley is about to tell them he only writes songs for her, when Robby agrees.

Miley confides in Lilly. What if he likes writing for guys more than he likes writing for Hannah? When Robby comes home two hours late she's mad at him.

ROBBY: Oh, I'm sorry, honey, but the time just got away from us. One minute we're spitballing song ideas, the next thing I know we're having a spitball fight. Then we started playing air hockey and video games. It was a regular P-A-R-T-Y ... party.

MILEY: You said you were working.

ROBBY: Well, it turns out I was. Listen to this. (Robby sings) Well, it's a lot cooler when the Jo-Bros do it.

MILEY: The Jo-Bros? (turns to Lilly) He's even got a pet name for them.

LILLY: Oh, come on, I'm sure he has a pet name for you, too.

MILEY: Yeah, Miley.

ROBBY: You know, I know it's not the way that I usually work but goofing around with those boys is pulling a great song out of me. And look at this. (Robby puts his hand round the back of his head and grabs the corner of his mouth) Fish on a hook! Joe taught it to me. You're right, he's the funny one.

MILEY: Yeah, hilarious.

Next day, Robby is working on his song when Miley shoots a pea at him from a shooter. She's offering him an arm tootin' contest when Robby's mobile rings. He takes the call.

ROBBY: No, there's no one here by the name of Gunnar. Sorry, this ain't the Tinkle residence. Well, I don't care what you say, I'm not Gunnar Tinkle. Gonna tinkle? Joe, is that you?

JONAS BROS: We so own you! That was sick!

ROBBY: Oh, you boys. L-O-L.

MILEY: You know L-O-L?

ROBBY: Yeah. Nick taught it to me.

Robby tells Miley he's going to meet the boys so they can finish the song. Lilly shows up on her skateboard.

LILLY: Oh my gosh. Your dad's having a bro-mance.

MILEY: Worse, he's having a Jo-bro-mance. I used to be the one that he loved to write for.

Miley has an idea: the Jonas Brothers wouldn't want the song if they thought Robby had stolen it from another band! Miley and Lilly dress up as guys and they're in the studio when the Jonas Brothers arrive!

NICK: This is Joe and Kevin. And I'm Nick.

MILEY: (puts on a 'guy voice') We know who you are. Your music rocks.

LILLY: And you're so hot. (awkward moment)

MILEY: On the charts. Burning them up. (Miley covers for her)

LILLY: Yeah! That's what I meant. Dudes. Yo.

KEVIN: Who are you guys?

MILEY: I'm Mi ... lo. Milo.

LILLY: And I'm Otis.

MILEY: Right. We're Milo and ... Otis.

JOE: So, what are you guys working on?

LILLY: New song we just wrote ourselves.
We wrote it. Milo and Otis.
Two guys. Football!

MILEY: They get it. Let's play it for them.

LILLY: Coolio. Monster Trucks!

Miley and Lilly sing the song Robby wrote for the Jonas Brothers.

JOE: That's ... That's our song! Isn't it?

KEVIN: I can't hear you. My ears are full of melted brain.

NICK: I kind of liked it.

The Jonas Brothers tell 'Milo' and 'Otis' that it's their song.

MILEY: Robby Ray didn't write that song. He stole it from us. He came in while we were rehearsing and said he was just listening.

KEVIN: Unbelievable.

NICK: He ripped you off?

MILEY: Totally.

The Brothers are really mad because they think Robby has lied to them. At that moment, Robby walks in. 'Milo' and 'Otis' squirm. That evening, Miley and Robby have a heart-to-heart. She tells him she thinks the song is really good but she's worried that if he writes for other people he won't have time for her.

ROBBY: I could write a hundred songs for those boys but there's one thing I couldn't do, that's put my arm around them and say they're my little girl ... Well, I could, but it'd be extremely weird.

MILEY: So you're not bored with me?

ROBBY: Bored with you? I love writing songs for Hannah Montana. Almost as much as I love being Miley's daddy. You know it's a shame you didn't like those boys though. I had this vision about getting them and Hannah –

MILEY: Hold on, Pops. I said I didn't like them spending so much time with you. Now, with me? That would be off the hook! Get it? Off the hook! (Miley does the fish-on-a-hook impression)

Y'all know how it ends? Well, Hannah and the Jonas Brothers went back to the studio and recorded the song together.

Can I Have Your

Your handwriting can say a lot about you. Find out what hidden secrets it can reveal. Write: 'The quick brown fox jumps over the lazy dog' in your own handwriting below.

....

....

....

Big, rounded letters, especially o, a and s

You're open to new ideas and will have a go at anything.

Small, thin letters

You're a bit shy in a big group and prefer to hang around with one or two best friends.

Autograph?

Right-sloping letters
You have strong feelings and emotions.

Joining all the letters
If your letters are clear and all joined, then you're a very tidy and organised person.

The dot on the i
If it's precisely placed above the letter, then you're a perfectionist.

If it's before or after the letter, then you tend to be a little impatient.

Mixed sloping letters
You can be a little unpredictable at times.

Hearts, circles or stars on the i.
If you draw on top of the i, then you want to be the centre of attention.

LARGE CAPITAL LETTERS
You're very confident in your abilities.

Underlining your name in your signature
You're a diva who wants to be noticed!

Big loops
You're popular and always doing fun stuff with your mates.

STRAIGHT-UP LETTERS
You hide your feelings and emotions.

Even-sized letters
You're totally reliable and others know they can depend on your loyalty and friendship.

Left-sloping letters
You try not to feel emotional.

FANCY CAPITAL LETTERS
You're a bit of a drama queen.

Fruit and

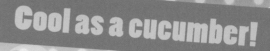

If you and your family and friends were fruit and veg, which type would you all be? Write the names under the foods that best describe yourself and the people you know.

Cool as a cucumber!

You're so easy-going, nothing ever fazes you. Even when disaster strikes, you can still see the funny side! After all, it's why everyone wants to hang out with you.

That's ...

....

Sweet as a cherry!

Your warm and bubbly personality is totally infectious. You're smart and talented but you can act crazy sometimes. It's almost like there are two sides to you!

That's ...

....

Which one sounds suspiciously like Miley?

46

Veggie People

Hot like a chilli pepper!

You know exactly what you want and you go for it! But sometimes your hot temper can get the better of you when things don't go as you planned.

That's ...

....

Prickly like a pineapple!

Your tough and prickly skin hides a softer and sweeter inside. Your sharp tongue tells it like it is, but others know they can count on you when it matters.

That's ...

....

Knobbly like a potato!

You're not perfect – but, hey, who is? You mess up sometimes and your ideas often get 'mashed' but you're ever the optimist – that's what we all love about you!

That's ...

....

Green like a kiwi fruit!

You're sassy and totally talented but your uncontrollable jealous streak can sometimes get you into a lot of trouble.

That's ...

....

Secret Wish

You can make a secret wish for a special friend and hide it for them to find in this gorgeous gift.

You will need:

- felt in two colours
- embroidery thread and needle
- cotton wool for stuffing
- tiny paper square
- a sequin or button for decoration
- ribbon for hanging

What you do:

1.

Cut out two star shapes from felt. Cut a smaller star from felt of a different colour.

2. Leave a secret pocket!

NOW HERE'S THE SECRET PART: you sew the small star to one of the big stars with little running stitches but you don't go through both layers at the top.

3.

Sew the two big stars together, stuffing the inside with cotton wool before finishing the stitches.

4.

Write a secret wish for your friend on a tiny piece of paper and tuck it inside the pocket behind the little star.

5.

Sew a loop of ribbon to the top for hanging and decorate with a sequin or button.

Give to your special friend!

Who Said That?

Match these quotes to the characters who said them.

1.

"SO ... YOU'RE NOT INTO ME AT ALL! NOT EVEN A LITTLE? IT'S ONLY BEEN A COUPLE OF MONTHS. WHAT ARE YOU, MADE OF STONE?"

Robby

Miley

2.

"MAN, I MEAN, YOU DON'T WANT TO BE A COUPLE AND WHEN I TRY TO BE FRIENDS YOU ALMOST WRECK MY MOVIE. WHAT AM I GONNA DO WITH YOU?"

Jackson

3.

"JUST FOR THAT, I'M GONNA TELL THEM HOW YOU USED TO PUT THAT DIAPER ON YOUR HEAD AND RUN AROUND THE HOUSE ... CAPTAIN DIAPER HEAD!"

Lilly

4.

"... I'M JUST A SIDEKICK WHO NEEDS TO LEARN HOW TO SAY, NO."

Jake

5.

"WE'RE GUYS. WE'RE NOT SUPPOSED TO SHOWER EVERY DAY. THAT'S WHAT MAGAZINE COLOGNE SAMPLES ARE FOR."

Answers on page 68.

H-A-N-N-A-H

Here's an acrostic poem that uses the letters in Hannah's name.

H ot clothes

A mazing performer

N aturally talented

N ever, ever dull

A wesome best friend

H appy personality

Now make up an acrostic poem for Miley. When you're done, try making ones for you and a friend below!

M ....

I ....

L ....

E ....

Y ....

Doodle Sudoku

Grab a pencil and complete this sudoku with Hannah's favourite doodles! Complete the grid so that each doodle only appears once in each row and column.

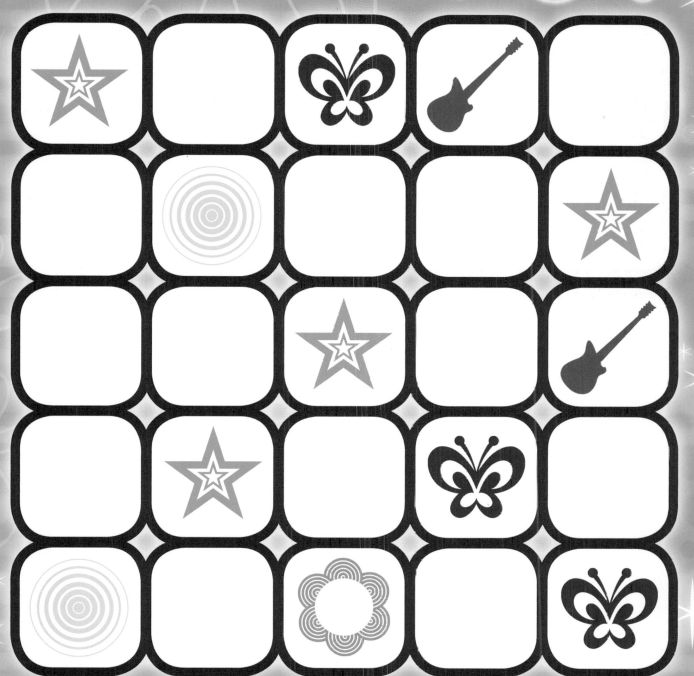

Answers on page 68.

53

Secret Script

This is a fun game to play with a friend who loves Hannah Montana as much as you do.

You only need:

- a sheet of paper and a pen or pencil each
- lots of crazy ideas!

Here's what you do:

- Fold a sheet of paper into three sections.

- In the top section, write the beginning of a Hannah storyline. Keep what you've written a secret by folding the section back so that your friend can't see it.

- Now get your friend to write the middle of the story and fold this over as well so that you can't see it.

- Finally, you get to write the ending!

- Open up and enjoy reading the hilarious results!

One day, Miley and Lilly ...

Then Jackson came home ...

In the end it ...

Secret Superstar

Find your way to the centre of this star maze.

START

Answer on page 68.

A Word from Lilly

Lilly is a loyal friend, who sure has a way with words ...

But subtle, she's not!

Once, when Jake was at Miley's house:

JAKE: Did I tell you guys that already?

MILEY: You might have mentioned it once or twice ...

LILLY: Or 30 times!

Quote from 'Achy Jakey Heart Part 2'

When Hannah couldn't think of a way to break up with Jake, Lilly came straight up with a couple of her own ideas:

1. Move to Peru.

2. Have a face transplant.

Quote from 'Achy Jakey Heart Part 2'

You can't rely on Lilly to keep cool under pressure ...

When Miley and Lilly went on the set of Jake's new movie:

MILEY: So, where's Mikayla?

JAKE: Er, in make-up. Why?

LILLY: Oh, we just wanted to wish her luck. It's not like we're here to get her fired or anything! That's ... that's crazy talk!

Quote from 'That's What Friends Are For'

But you can guarantee she'll make you laugh when you're having a bad time ...

Miley, mad at Robby for spending time with the Jonas Brothers, was braiding Lilly's hair:

LILLY: Ow! You're braiding hair not starting a chainsaw!

MILEY: I'm sorry, but they're guys and he's a guy, and what if he figures out that he likes writing for guys more than he likes writing for Hannah?

LILLY: Well, then you'll be out of work and I'll be bald!

Quote from 'Me and Mr Jonas and Mr Jonas and Mr Jonas'

Write your favourite quote from Lilly here:

....

....

....

....

....

....

....

Quote from:
....

....

STYLE STATEMENT

You're going out with your mates to a pizza restaurant and maybe you'll catch a movie later. But what do you wear? Tick your fave choices then check out your style statement.

What would you wear ...?

1
 strappy top
 bright t-shirt
 stripy shirt

2
 mini skirt
 cut-off jeans
 pencil skirt

3
 glittery shrug
 hoodie
 smart jacket

4
 high wedges
 ballet pumps
 kitten heels

5
 sparkly gemstones
 bangles and beads
 string of pearls

6
 sparkly lipgloss
 fruity lipbalm
 red lipstick

7 ☆ glittery nail art

🦋 pink nail varnish

❀ French manicure

8 ☆ tumbling curls

🦋 tousled waves

❀ smooth and sleek

Mainly ☆

You're a girl who goes for glitter and glamour every time. It's a high-maintenance style but you always want to look sensational – even when walking the dog! Hannah would love your style choices and, who knows, one day you might be walking the red carpet yourself.

Mainly 🦋

Your confident and casual styling shows off your natural beauty and charm. You go for colour, layering and individual style to create a look that's all your own. You're creative, adventurous and great fun to be with and, like Lilly, everyone enjoys having you around.

Mainly ❀

Classic chic is your fave look. It's an expensive option but this style won't ever date. You're smart and sophisticated in pinstripes, hot heels and elegant designer gear. 'Dress For Success' is your motto! Success might mean owning this pizza restaurant one day – so watch out, Rico, this girl's serious competition.

Hannah Sleepover

Check out these ideas for a rockin' Hannah Montana-themed sleepover.

Ask your friends to come dressed as either Miley or Hannah and make sure you have loads of her CDs, DVDs and books. Turn on your favourite track – now for some rockin' Hannah games!

Secret Hannah

This is like Secret Santa! Ask your friends to wrap up a small, token gift to bring to the sleepover, keeping the contents a secret. Later, you can give out the gifts or use them as prizes for the best-dressed Hannah or Miley.

Guess Who's Miley?

One of your friends goes out of the room while the others agree who is going to be 'Miley'. Then invite your friend back – but don't tell them who Miley is! When Miley winks (secretively) at one of the others they should start dancing immediately as if they were Hannah. The friend who's come back into the room has to guess who Miley is!

In the Manner of Hannah

Take some favourite quotes from Hannah Montana shows and write them on separate pieces of star-shaped card. Write different adverbs (eg softly, croakily, angrily, impatiently, sleepily) on guitar-shaped pieces of card. Shuffle the cards and turn them over so that no one sees what's written on them. Get your friends to take turns to choose a star and a guitar card and read out the quote in the way described by the adverb. The others have to guess what the adverb is!

Pin the Wig on Miley

Draw a full length picture of Miley on a large sheet of paper. Draw or make a blonde 'wig' from a piece of yellow paper or use beige wool. Attach a drawing pin to the wig. Get your friends to take turns to try to put the wig on Miley's head! The problem is, they have to do it blindfolded! The one that gets closest to placing the wig correctly is the winner.

Hannah Charades

Hannah Montana song titles or show titles are great for charades. Write the titles on to card and take turns to mime the words to each title. Open palms indicate a song title, and a rectangle shape, drawn in the air, indicates a TV show. Count on your fingers to indicate the number of words. Then break words down to mime separate syllables. Show the number of syllables by tapping your fingers on your arm.

Get Hannah's

Transform a boring old T-shirt or vest with inspiration from Hannah Montana's latest new look.

You will need:

- a plain T-shirt or vest
- felt or fabric in contrasting colours
- sequins
- sewing needle and thread, or fabric glue
- scissors

What you do:

1.

Cut out randomly-shaped pieces of felt or fabric. Arrange the shapes and sequins in an abstract way to decorate the front of your vest.

New Look

2.

Use lots of sequins – the more the better for a sparkly effect!

3.

Glue the fabric and sequins in place using fabric glue, or sew them on.

Top tip!

It's easy to sew the sequins on – and it's much more fun than gluing! Here's how:

• Thread a needle with fine cotton and knot the end. Push the needle up through the inside of the vest, the fabric piece and through the tiny hole in the sequin.

• Now push the needle back down through the layers to the inside of the vest. Knot the end to secure.

DISCOVER YOUR

Find out more about your secret self and reveal your true identity. It could be the key to your future career!

For each question, circle the statement that is most like you.

1. You mainly hang about with:

a) one best mate

b) your family

c) a group of friends

2. With friends, you love to:

a) give each other makeovers

b) play games and watch DVDs

c) party to your fave music

3. Your fave subjects at school are:

a) art and design

b) English, maths and sciences

c) sports, music, dance and drama

4. When you're bored you:

a) doodle and draw

b) read a good book

c) text your friends

SECRET SELF!

5. At home, you spend most of your time:

a) making all kinds of stuff

b) doing your homework

c) watching TV or playing computer games

6. Your ambition for the future is to:

a) do something you love

b) set up your own business

c) be famous

7. Your best birthday treat would be:

a) an activity day spent with your mates

b) going to see the latest movie

c) having a big noisy party

Count how many a's, b's and c's to reveal your identity!

a's ☐   b's ☐   c's ☐

Mostly a's

Your head is buzzing with ideas. You're highly creative and practical. You love to surround yourself with beautiful things and probably chose your bedroom's colour scheme and accessories!

Future career: artist; architect; art teacher; graphic artist; fashion, interior or textiles designer.

Mostly b's

You're a deep thinker and a bit of a brainiac. You're not happy until you find out how everything in the world works. You love doing puzzles – you probably love doing your homework, too!

Future career: author; journalist; accountant; company or film director; doctor; research scientist; IT consultant; lawyer; teacher.

Mostly c's

You're popular, talented and totally fun to be with. You have more friends (or is that 'fans') than you can count! You love being in the spotlight. Could you be a secret Hannah Montana?

Future career: celebrity; pop star; actor; theatre producer; dancer; choreographer; politician; TV or radio presenter.

Memory Game

Can you remember these 10 images? Study the photos below for just 30 seconds (get someone to time you), close the book and describe each photo.

To help you remember, try to imagine Hannah in a crazy new episode where these items figure in some way.

1. Tied up!

2. New wig!

3. Silver boots!

4. Er, nice hat!

6. Cheese jerky!

5. Freaky!

7. Great guitar!

8. Awesome music award!

9. Suits you, Jake!

10. Dog tired!

ANSWERS

16 Hannah's World

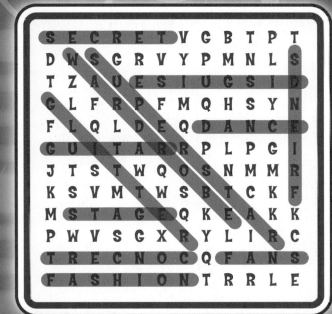

17 Guitar Girl

There are 10 guitars.

18-19 Superstar Doubles

20-23
That's What Friends Are For

1. Miley, 2. Jake, 3. Miley, 4. Jake, 5. Lilly,
6. Mikayla, 7. Miley, 8. Mikayla, 9. Jake,
10. Mikayla, 11. Miley, 12. Jake, 13. Miley,
14. Mikayla, 15. Miley, 16. Mikayla.

26-27 Trivia Tick Test

1. *b*, 2. *a*, 3. *c*, 4. *a*, 5. *b*, 6. *a*, 7. *b*, 8. *c*,
9. *a*, 10. *c*.

30-31 The Wrong Songs

1. Make Some Noise, **2.** We Got The Party,
3. Nobody's Perfect, **4.** Rock Star, **5.** Old
Blue Jeans, **6.** You And Me Together,
7. One In A Million, **8.** True Friend.

50-51 Who Said That?

1. Miley in *That's What Friends are For*,
2. Jake in *That's What Friends are For*,
3. Robby in *I Will Always Loathe You*,
4. Lilly in *That's What Friends are For*,
5. Jackson in *That's What Friends are For*.

53 Doodle Sudoku

55 Secret Superstar

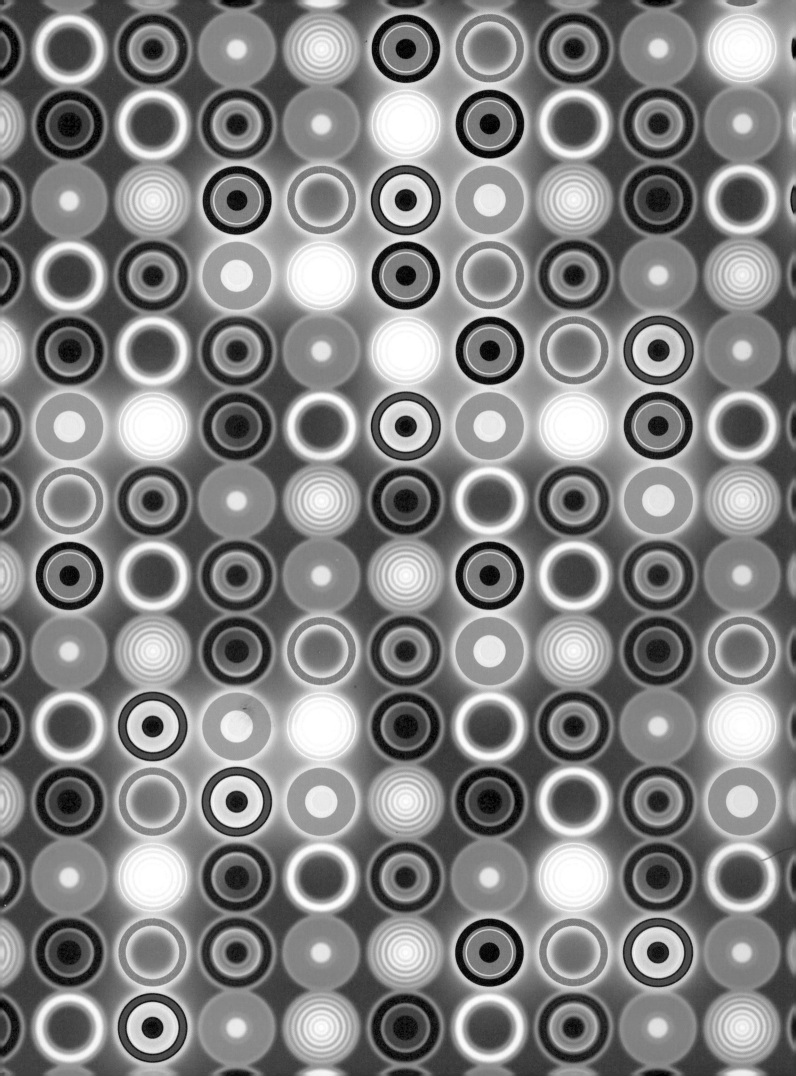